A Teddy Horsley Book

The Sunny Morning

by Leslie J Francis and Nicola M Slee

Pictures by Ferelith Eccles Williams

The Bear facts:
The Teddy Horsley Bible Series is designed to build bridges between the young child's day to day experiences of the world and major biblical themes and stories.

Both authors work in church-related institutions of education. Nicola Slee is Director of Studies at the Aston Training Scheme in Birmingham. Leslie Francis is Professor of Pastoral Theology at the University of Wales, Lampeter and Trinity College, Carmarthen.

The Teddy Horsley Series is a result of both authors' extensive research into the religious development of young children, and their wide experience of educational work in schools and churches.

Published by:
National Christian Education Council, 1020 Bristol Road, Selly Oak, Birmingham, B29 6LB

British Library Cataloguing-In Publication Data:
A catalogue record for this book is available from the British Library.

Text © Leslie J Francis and Nicola M Slee 1983
Illustrations © National Christian Education Council 1994

All rights reserved. No part of this publication may be reproduced, stored in a retrieval system, or transmitted, in any form or by any means, electronic, mechanical, photocopied, recorded or otherwise without the prior permission of the National Christian Education Council.

Unless otherwise stated, quotations from the Bible are from the Good News Bible, published by the Bible Societies/Collins, © American Bible Society, New York, 1966, 1971, 1976.

First published 1989 Reprinted 1990, 1995 ISBN 0-7197-0843-5 Printed in England

It is a warm, sunny morning and Teddy Horsley feels full of life.

He skips into the open fields

with Lucy, Walter and Betsy Bear.

He sees the lambs gambolling on the grass.

He hears the birds singing in the sky.

He runs after the rabbits playing on the path

and stops to talk to the sleepy hedgehog.

He stretches up tall to see the leaves on the trees

and bends down low to touch the wild flowers.

He jumps in the morning air

and runs about in the warm sunshine.

Teddy Horsley shares in the new life of the morning.

It is Easter Sunday and Teddy Horsley feels full of life.

He skips into the church

with Lucy, Walter and Betsy Bear.

He sees the Easter garden.

He hears the good news of the Resurrection.

He runs to enter the empty tomb

and stops to touch the folded clothes.

He stretches up tall to see the flame of the Paschal candle

and bends down low to touch the waters of Baptism.

Teddy Horsley shares in the new life of Easter.

In *The Sunny Morning*, Teddy Horsley experiences the joys of new life when he meets the lambs, birds, rabbits, and hedgehog, and when he sees the leaves and wild flowers growing in the fresh air. His experiences of the new life of the sunny morning help him to share in the Christians' celebration of the new life of Easter.

Early on Sunday morning, while it was still dark, Mary Magdalene went to the tomb and saw that the stone had been taken away from the entrance. She went running to Simon Peter and the other disciple, whom Jesus loved, and told them, ''They have taken the Lord from the tomb, and we don't know where they have put him!''

Then Peter and the other disciple went to the tomb. The two of them were running, but the other disciple ran faster than Peter and reached the tomb first. He bent over and saw the linen wrappings, but he did not go in. Behind him came Simon Peter, and he went straight into the tomb. He saw the linen wrappings lying there and the cloth which had been round Jesus' head. It was not lying with the linen wrappings but was rolled up by itself. Then the other disciple, who had reached the tomb first, also went in; he saw and believed.

John 20.1-8

The following questions suggest further ways of developing the links between the young child's experience, the story, and the Bible passage.

Talk about sunny mornings:
When have you been out on a sunny morning?
Who did you meet?
What did you do?
Did you see any animals and birds?
Did you see any trees and plants?
How did you feel on the sunny morning?

Talk about the story:
What creatures does Teddy Horsley meet in the open fields, on the grass, and in the sky?
Who does Teddy Horsley stop to talk to?
How does Teddy Horsley feel on the sunny morning?
What does Teddy Horsley see in the church?
How does Teddy Horsley feel in the church?